A New Day

COVER ILLUSTRATOR

Spotlight

Keith Baker

▼ Keith Baker likes to share his stories and art with children. For the cover of *A New Day,* he has created a simple world, showing buildings, creatures, and plants from many different places. The painting tells us that it is always a new day in some place in this world. Each new day children open this book, they will read a story from some special place around the world.

Acknowledgments appear on page 256, which constitutes an extension of this copyright page.

ISBN 0-663-54650-8

New Dimensions
IN THE
WORLD OF READING

A New Day

P R O G R A M   A U T H O R S

James F. Baumann   Roselmina Indrisano   P. David Pearson
Theodore Clymer   Dale D. Johnson   Taffy E. Raphael
Carl Grant   Connie Juel   Marian Davies Toth
Elfrieda H. Hiebert   Jeanne R. Paratore   Richard L. Venezky

SILVER BURDETT GINN

NEEDHAM, MA   MORRISTOWN, NJ

ATLANTA, GA   DALLAS, TX   DEERFIELD, IL   MENLO PARK, CA

Unit 1 Theme

Friends Forever

Unit 2 Theme

STORYTELLERS

6

Friends Forever

We meet friends in school.
We meet friends in books.

What makes a friend a friend?

DIGGING ON THE SANDS, *ceramic tile, early 20th century*

Theme Books for
Friends Forever

What do friends do for us?

✳ In the book *Wilfrid Gordon McDonald Partridge* by Mem Fox, a young boy helps his favorite person find her memory.

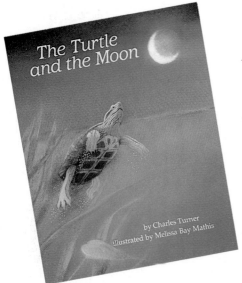

✳ In *The Turtle and the Moon* by Charles Turner, a turtle makes a special friend who plays with him at night.

* Cristina's friends think they've been tricked in *Showtime!* by Jared Jansen. But Pablo surprises them!

* Josephine goes to school in *Josephine Finds a Friend* by D. Marion.

* In *Toby Is My Best Friend* by Anna Kate Winsey, two friends surprise each other at a costume party.

* Can Grandpa and Noodle ever be friends? Find out in *Room for Two* by Lizanne Wertzer.

YOUR FRIEND, LITTLE BEAR

from *Little Bear's Friend*

written by Else Holmelund Minarik
illustrated by Maurice Sendak

Summer was over,
and Emily was saying good-by.
It was time to go
back to school.

Mother Bear baked a cake.
Little Bear made lemonade.

Mother Bear said,
"Let us eat up all the cake.
If we do, then it will not
rain tomorrow."

"Let it rain," said Little Bear.
"Emily will not be here tomorrow
to play with me."

"Anyhow," said Emily,
"we can eat up the cake.
And we can drink the lemonade."

So they ate the cake,
and drank the lemonade,
and talked and talked.

Then it was time
for Emily to go home.

Father Bear said,
"Don't let Lucy break
any more arms."

"Oh, no," said Emily.

Emily hugged her doll, and said,
"Lucy wants to say good-by, too.
Say good-by to Little Bear, Lucy."

Emily made Little Bear hold Lucy.

Then she said to him,
"Little Bear, you can have Lucy
for keeps.
I will give her to you."

"Oh—" began Little Bear.

But before he could say anything,
Emily took Lucy back again.

"Oops!" she said. "I forgot.
Lucy has to come to school with me."

Emily opened her pocketbook.
She took out a fine new pen.
"This is for you," she said.
"I want you to have it."

Little Bear took the pen.
"Thank you, Emily," he said.

He ran into his room,
and came back with a pretty toy boat.

"This is for you," he said.
"For keeps. You can sail it
in your bathtub."

20

"Thank you," said Emily. "I will.
Good-by, Little Bear.
See you next summer."

Little Bear stood at the door
till Emily was out of sight.
Two big tears ran down his face.

21

Mother Bear saw them,
and took him on her lap.

"My goodness, Little Bear," she said.
"You will be going to school, too,
and you will learn to write.
Then you can write to Emily."

"Little Bear can begin right now,"
said Father Bear.
He got out some paper, and said,
"Little Bear can write his own name."

"Yes," said Mother Bear,
"with his fine new pen."

She took Little Bear's paw in hers,
and helped him to begin—

That made Little Bear very happy.

He said,
"When can I write to Emily?"

"Soon," said Mother Bear.

And soon he did write to Emily,
like this:

    Dear Emily,

       It is snowing.
       I love the snow.
       I wish I could send you some.
       Owl, Duck, Hen and Cat
       send their love.
       So do the ducklings.
       I cannot wait for summer.

          Your friend,

             Little Bear.

Reader's Response ～ Do you think that Emily's gift was a good gift for Little Bear? What gift would you give Little Bear?

THE FIRST DAY OF SCHOOL

Little Bear wants to start school so he can write to Emily. Do you think he learned to write a letter on his first day?

What does happen on the first day of school? In Russia, children bring flowers for their teacher.

What happened on your first day?

We Are **BEST** Friends

written and illustrated by Aliki

Peter came to tell Robert the news.
"I am moving away," he said.

"You can't move away," said Robert.
"We are best friends."

"I am moving far away," said Peter.

"What will you do without me?"
asked Robert.
"Who will you play with?"

"We will live in a new house," said Peter.

"You will miss my birthday party!"
said Robert.

"I will be going to a new school,"
said Peter.

"Who will you fight with?" asked Robert.
"Nobody fights like best friends."

"I will make new friends," said Peter.

"You can't move away," said Robert.
"You will miss me too much."

But Peter moved away.

There was nothing to do without Peter.
There was no one to play with.

There was no one to share with.

There was no one to fight with.
Not the way best friends fight.
There was no fun anymore.

"I'll bet Peter doesn't even remember me,"
said Robert. "It's a good thing he's not here.
I'd have to punch him one."

"Hello. My name is Will," said a new face.

I don't like freckles, thought Robert.

"I used to go to another school," said Will.

I don't like glasses, thought Robert.

"My friends are all there," said Will.

I don't like silly names like Will,
thought Robert.

"It was fun," said Will.
"Not boring like this place."

A letter came for Robert.
A letter from Peter.

DEAR ROBERT,
I HOPE YOU STILL REMEMBER ME.
I LIKE MY NEW HOUSE NOW.
I LIKE MY NEW SCHOOL NOW.
AT FIRST I DIDN'T LIKE ANYTHING.
BUT NOW I HAVE A FRIEND, ALEX.
YOU ARE MY BEST FRIEND,
BUT ALEX IS NICE.

IT IS FUN TO HAVE SOMEONE
TO PLAY WITH AGAIN.
IT'S NOT SO LONELY.
                LOVE, PETER

Robert drew Peter a letter.
He drew two friends building a fort.
He drew them playing with their cars.
He drew them riding their bikes.
He wrote:

IF YOU WERE HERE,
THIS IS WHAT WE'D BE DOING.
BUT YOU'RE NOT.

Then he wrote:

THERE IS A NEW BOY IN SCHOOL.
HE HAS FRECKLES.

Robert saw Will by the fence.
"Did you lose something?" he asked.

"I thought I saw a frog," said Will.

"That's funny, looking for a frog,"
said Robert.

"What's funny about it?
I like frogs," said Will.

"I used to have a pet frog named Greenie.
He'd wait for me by the pond near where I
lived. He must miss me a lot."

"I know where there are frogs,"
said Robert.
"Right in my garden."

"You're just saying that,"
said Will.

"I mean it," said Robert.
"You can see
for yourself."

"If I had a frog
in my garden,
I'd share it,"
said Will.

"That's what
I'm doing,"
said Robert.

Robert and Will rode home together.
They went straight into the garden.
The frogs were there.
One leaped under a bush, and
Will caught it.

"I'll call you Greenie the Second,"
he said.
"You like me already, don't you?"

"The frogs lay their eggs here every year,"
said Robert.
"It's almost time.
My friend Peter used to come
watch the tadpoles.
He called them Inkywiggles.
He'll miss them."

"Why?" asked Will.

"He moved away," said Robert.
"Just about the time you came.
I write him letters."

"Then you can write about the
Inkywiggles," said Will.

They laughed.

"I haven't had so much fun since I moved
here," said Will.

"Neither have I," said Robert.

40

Robert wrote to Peter.

Dear Peter,
I can't wait until summer
when you come to visit.
The new boy is called Will.
I showed him the frogs.
He had a pet one near his home.
But he had to move away, like you.
He thinks Inkywiggles is funny.
I'll write when they hatch.

Love, Robert.

P.S. How is Alex?
P.P.S. See you soon.

Robert mailed the letter,
then rode over to Will's house to play.

Reader's Response ～ How would you
feel if your best friend moved away?

Library Link ～ *Look in the library for these
books written and illustrated by Aliki:* Digging
Up Dinosaurs *and* Feelings.

The Pony Express

Letters were not always sent the way they are today. In the Old West, there were no cars, planes, or mailboxes. Mail was carried by steamship, stage coach, or, for a short time, by Pony Express riders on horseback.

Many of the riders were teenagers. They were not heavy, so the horses could run fast and not get tired. Each teenager rode about seventy-five miles or more and then gave the mail to the next rider.

Do you think it was an exciting job?

Poem

by Langston Hughes

I loved my friend.
He went away from me.
There's nothing more to say.
The poem ends,
Soft as it began—
I loved my friend.

Alone

from *Days with Frog and Toad*

written and illustrated
by Arnold Lobel

Toad went to Frog's house.
He found a note on the door.
The note said,
"Dear Toad, I am not at home.
I went out.
I want to be alone."

"Alone?" said Toad.
"Frog has me for a friend.
Why does he want to be alone?"

Toad looked through the windows.
He looked in the garden.
He did not see Frog.

Toad went to the woods.
Frog was not there.
He went to the meadow.
Frog was not there.
Toad went down to the river.
There was Frog.
He was sitting on an island
by himself.

"Poor Frog," said Toad.
"He must be very sad.
I will cheer him up."

Toad ran home.
He made sandwiches.
He made a pitcher
of iced tea.

He put everything
in a basket.

Toad hurried
back to the river.
"Frog," he shouted,
"it's me.
It's your best friend, Toad!"
Frog was too far away to hear.
Toad took off his jacket
and waved it like a flag.
Frog was too far away to see.
Toad shouted and waved,
but it was no use.

Frog sat on the island.
He did not see or hear Toad.

A turtle swam by.
Toad climbed on the turtle's back.
"Turtle," said Toad,
"carry me to the island.
Frog is there.
He wants to be alone."

"If Frog wants to be alone,"
said the turtle,
"why don't you leave him alone?"

"Maybe you are right," said Toad.
"Maybe Frog does not
want to see me.
Maybe he does not want me
to be his friend anymore."
"Yes, maybe," said the turtle
as he swam to the island.

"Frog!" cried Toad.
"I am sorry for all
the dumb things I do.
I am sorry for all
the silly things I say.
Please be my friend again!"
Toad slipped off the turtle.
With a splash,
he fell in the river.

Frog pulled Toad
up onto the island.
Toad looked in the basket.
The sandwiches were wet.
The pitcher of iced tea was empty.
"Our lunch is spoiled," said Toad.
"I made it for you, Frog,
so that you would be happy."

"But Toad," said Frog.
"I *am* happy. I am very happy.
This morning
when I woke up
I felt good because
the sun was shining.
I felt good because
I was a frog.
And I felt good because
I have you for a friend.
I wanted to be alone.
I wanted to think about
how fine everything is."

"Oh," said Toad.
"I guess that is a very good reason
for wanting to be alone."
"Now," said Frog,
"I will be glad *not* to be alone.
Let's eat lunch."

Frog and Toad
stayed on the island
all afternoon.
They ate wet sandwiches
without iced tea.
They were two close friends
sitting alone together.

Reader's Response ∿ What do you do with a good friend? What did Frog and Toad do together?

Library Link ∿ *"Alone" came from a book called* Days with Frog and Toad. *Look for it and other Frog and Toad books in your library.*

More Like Frog or Toad?

In this story, Frog wants to be alone. But Toad wants to be with his friend. Are you more like Frog or Toad?

Someone once asked Arnold Lobel that question. He said he was like both Frog and Toad. He said, "I think everybody is both."

Arnold Lobel says he puts a little of himself into all the animals and people in his books.

If you put yourself in a story, what animal would you like to be?

62

two friends

lydia and shirley have
two pierced ears and
two bare ones
five pigtails
two pairs of sneakers
two berets
two smiles
one necklace
one bracelet
lots of stripes and
one good friendship

Nikki Giovanni

Some Fun

written and
illustrated by

James Marshall

A dog and her goldfish were sitting
by the fire.

"I want to have some fun," said
the goldfish.

"But this is fun," said the dog.

"Not really," said the goldfish.
"I want to go places and see things.
I want to see the woods, the sky, and
the sea. I want to see some sharks!"

"Oh, very well," said the dog.

"This is very kind of you," said
the goldfish.

"Anything to keep you happy,"
said the dog. "But we can't go too far
from home. We don't want to get lost."

"Where will we go first?" asked
the goldfish.

"I know a place to see some
sharks," said the dog. "It's not far."

"Oh my!" cried the goldfish.
"Sharks! Look at their teeth!
This is really fun!"

"I'm glad you think so," said
the dog. "Can we go home now?"

"Oh, no!" cried the goldfish.
"I want to do more! I want
to see the sea."

"Anything to keep you happy,"
said the dog.

"Look at the waves!" cried the goldfish. "This is really fun!"

But the dog didn't like the sea. "The waves make me feel sick," she said. "Can we go home now?"

"Oh, no!" said the goldfish. "I want to see the sky. I want to fly."

"Anything to keep you happy," said the dog.

"This is really fun!" cried the goldfish. "Look at all the hills!"

But the dog did not like to fly. "I can't look down," she said. "I can't. Can we go home now?"

"Oh no!" said the goldfish. "Before we go home, we must see the woods."

"Anything to keep you happy," said the dog.

"Oh, my!" cried the goldfish.
"Look at all the trees."

The two friends looked all around
the woods. Before long they were lost.

"I'm sorry," said the dog.
"I don't know how to get home."

"Are you lost?" asked a kind elephant.

"Yes, we are," said the goldfish.

"Then I'll take you home," said
the elephant.

"This is very kind of you," said the dog.

"It's fun to go places and see things,"
said the elephant. "But it's good to go
home, too."

"Yes, it is," said the dog.

Before long the dog and her goldfish
were home.

"That was so much fun," said the goldfish. "Where can we go now?"

"We can sit at home by the fire," said the dog. "That's what I want to do."

"Anything to keep you happy," said the goldfish.

"You are very kind," said the dog.

Reader's Response ⌣ What do you do to make your friends happy?

To See the Sky

Like the goldfish in the story, Amelia Earhart liked adventures. As a girl, she once built a home-made roller coaster. When she grew up, she learned to fly a plane. She was the first woman to fly across the Atlantic Ocean alone. She won prizes and she met royalty. But for her the best part of flying was trying something new.

Do you ever dream about going on an adventure?

Together

by Anne Rockwell

Carol is my best friend. We always work and play together. Carol is blind. She cannot see, but Carol can do other things. She is a good storyteller. When she tells stories, I write the words for her. Then I draw pictures to go with her words. I tell Carol what the pictures look like.

Carol can play the guitar. I love to hear
her play. Sometimes I try to play the
guitar, too. Carol helps me. First she shows
me how to hold the guitar. Then she tells
me to feel the strings as I play. We play
and sing together.

Carol and I love to read together. I read with my eyes. Carol reads with her fingers. Her books are special. The words are made with dots. People who are blind feel the dots to read the words.

Carol shows me how she reads. I can feel the dots with my fingers. I try to read the dots, but I can't. Carol reads them for me.

Carol and I have our own garden. It is work to plant a garden. My dad helps. He finds seeds for us to plant.

First, we plant the seeds in the ground. Then we water them.
My dad helps us put water in the watering can. Sometimes I can't hold the watering can. Carol and I do it together.

Then we wait for the first plants to
come up. At last a little green plant
pops up out of the ground.
Carol and I run to tell my dad.
I tell Carol about the plant
and she feels it with her fingers.
It is a special day for us.

Carol and I love to work and play
together. We always have a lot of fun.
We are glad that we can share
so many special things.

Reader's Response ∽ What would
you like to share with Carol?

JASPER: A WORKING DOG

I'm Jasper, a Seeing Eye dog. I'm trained to help people like Carol. When I was a puppy, I lived with a nice family. Then I went to a special school and met my trainer. My trainer taught me to cross the street and turn right and left.

I finally met my new owner, Jan. We trained together and now we're a team. I use my eyes to lead Jan safely wherever she wants to go. Sometimes I'd like to play or chase birds, but I can't. Jan's my best friend so I must work to keep her safe.

Do you think Carol would like to have a Seeing Eye dog someday?

82

A HORSE NAMED GOLDFISH

by Mitchell Sharmat

Today is a big day. My mom and I are going to visit my cousin's farm. We get an early start and drive out of the city before the sun gets too hot. When Mom and I take a trip we like to sing songs and tell each other stories. But today I'm too excited to sing. I'm going to learn to ride a horse. This is really a big day!

Before long, the city is behind us. No more
tall buildings. Now we see horses and
cows and sheep.

"Are we there yet, Mom?" I keep asking.

"Almost," Mom answers. I think
she's tired of answering.

Soon we pull into a long, dusty road
and I see my cousin Terry's name
on the mailbox.

We park near the barn. Terry comes out
and waves. I start to run to him,
but I stop. There's a horse standing right
inside the door. And it's BIG.
I'm a little bit scared.
Terry knows how I feel.
He takes my hand.

"Try rubbing his nose, and
see how soft it feels," he says.

I'm still a little scared, but I rub
the horse's nose anyway.

"It's soft," I say.

"Talk softly to him," Terry says.

"Hi, Horse," I say quietly.

Then Terry tells me, "His name is Goldfish."

"Goldfish? That's a funny name for a horse."

"Well, Goldfish is a funny horse," says Terry.

After Goldfish and I get to know
each other a little better,
Terry asks me if I want to get on.

"Sure," I say. But I'm still scared.

When Terry helps me up,
I feel like a giant.

"Horses are sure tall," I say.

"They sure are," Terry says.

Terry takes Goldfish and me for a walk
and I'm not scared.
I think I'm going to like this horse.

Goldfish walks slowly. He seems to know
the way all by himself. He walks down a
little path right to the water and stops.
Terry helps me down. It's a long way to
the ground.

"Now watch this," Terry says.

Goldfish puts his big head way down to
the ground. Then he puts his nose under
the water and blows into it.

"Bubbles! He's blowing bubbles!"

"That's why I named him Goldfish," Terry
laughs. "He thinks he's a fish."

Goldfish and I spend all day getting to
know each other. After lunch, I even ride
without Terry's help. Not very far, though.
And by the end of the day, we're good
friends. I like riding Goldfish.

90

When it is almost dark, Mom calls me.

"Time to go home," she says.

"Can I come back soon
and ride Goldfish?" I ask.

"Sure," she says.

Goldfish rubs his nose against my arm.

"I think Goldfish has found a friend,"
Terry says.

"Me, too," I say.

Reader's Response ∼ Would you like to
ride Goldfish? Tell why or why not.

NAT LOVE, Cowboy

Did you know that many cowboys were African American?

The most famous African-American cowboy was Nat Love. He had been born into slavery, but was freed and became a cowboy. He knew all about riding and roping. He was also a sharp-shooter and a famous rodeo star.

Nat Love was a great storyteller. He told stories about Buffalo Bill and Jesse James, two famous cowboys. He even wrote a book of cowboy stories about his own life in the Old West.

12/13/04
QP

THE BEAR'S
TOOTHACHE

written and illustrated
by DAVID McPHAIL

One night I heard something
outside my window.

It was a bear
with a toothache.

I invited him in
and examined his teeth.

When I found the one that ached,
I tried to pull it out.
It wouldn't budge.

"Maybe some steak will loosen it
a little," said the bear.
So we went down to the kitchen,
where the bear chewed on some steak
and anything else he could find.
Pretty soon the food was all gone,
but the tooth was no looser
than before.

When we got back to my room,
I tried to hit the tooth with my pillow.
But the bear ducked,
and I hit the lamp instead
and knocked it to the floor.
Crash!

The noise woke my father,
who got up and came to my room.
"What happened to the lamp?"
he asked.
"It fell on the floor," I answered.
"Oh," he said,
and he went back to bed.

Then I had a good idea.
I tied one end of my cowboy rope
to the bear's tooth
and tied the other end to the bedpost.

102

Then the bear stood on the windowsill
and jumped.

And just as he hit the ground,
the tooth popped out!

The bear was so happy that
he gave me the tooth
to put under my pillow.

Reader's Response ∽ Do you think
the boy is a good storyteller? Tell why or
why not.

STORYTELLERS

What makes a story so special
that you want to hear it
over and over again?

LIBRARY II, 1960, painting by Jacob Lawrence, American, b. 1917. Egg tempera on hardboard. H. 23 1/2"; W. 29 1/2".
The Martin & Sarah Cherkasky Collection. Photo by Paul Macapi

Theme Books for Storytellers

Everyone has a story to share. What kinds of stories do you like to read or write?

✳ Sail with Max to an island and meet the wild things in **Where the Wild Things Are** by Maurice Sendak.

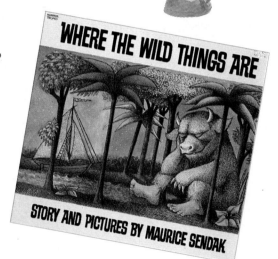

✳ Who will Mouse marry in **Mouse's Marriage** by Junko Morimoto—the sun, a cloud, the wind, a wall—or a mouse?

❋ Find out who makes beautiful shoes for the shoemaker in **The Elves and the Shoemaker**, retold by Deborah Eaton.

❋ Will the snow and ice ever melt in **A Winter's Nap** by Winston White?

❋ Read all kinds of poems in **Scrapbook** by Deborah Akers.

❋ Can Jackal beat Lion with his tricks? Read **The Lion and the Jackal** by Beverley Dietz to find out.

Worlds I Know

by Myra Cohn Livingston

Once upon a time

I can read the pictures
by myself
in the books that lie
on the lowest shelf.
I know the place
where the stories start
and some I can even say
by heart,
and I make up adventures
and dreams and words
for some of the pages
I've never heard.

111

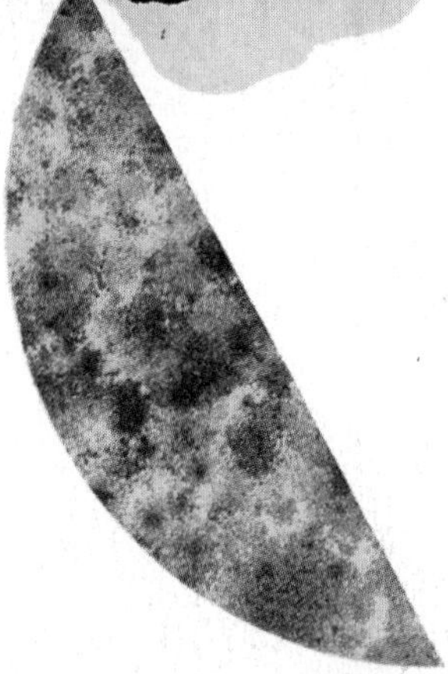

But I like it best
when Mother sits
and reads to me
my favorites;
when Rapunzel pines
and the prince comes forth,
or the Snow Queen sighs
in the bitter north;
when Rose Red snuggles
against the bear,
and I lean against Mother
and feel her hair.

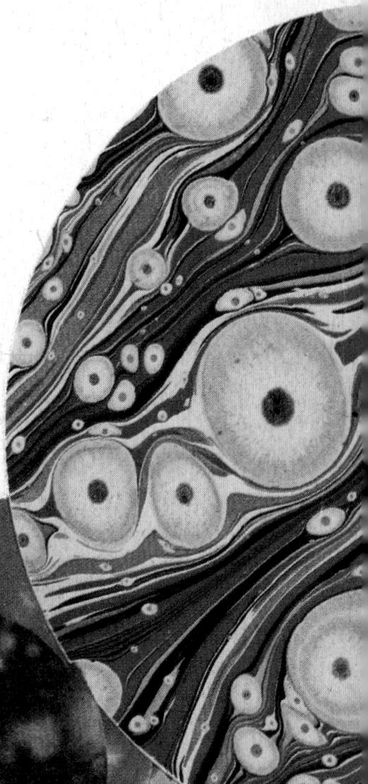

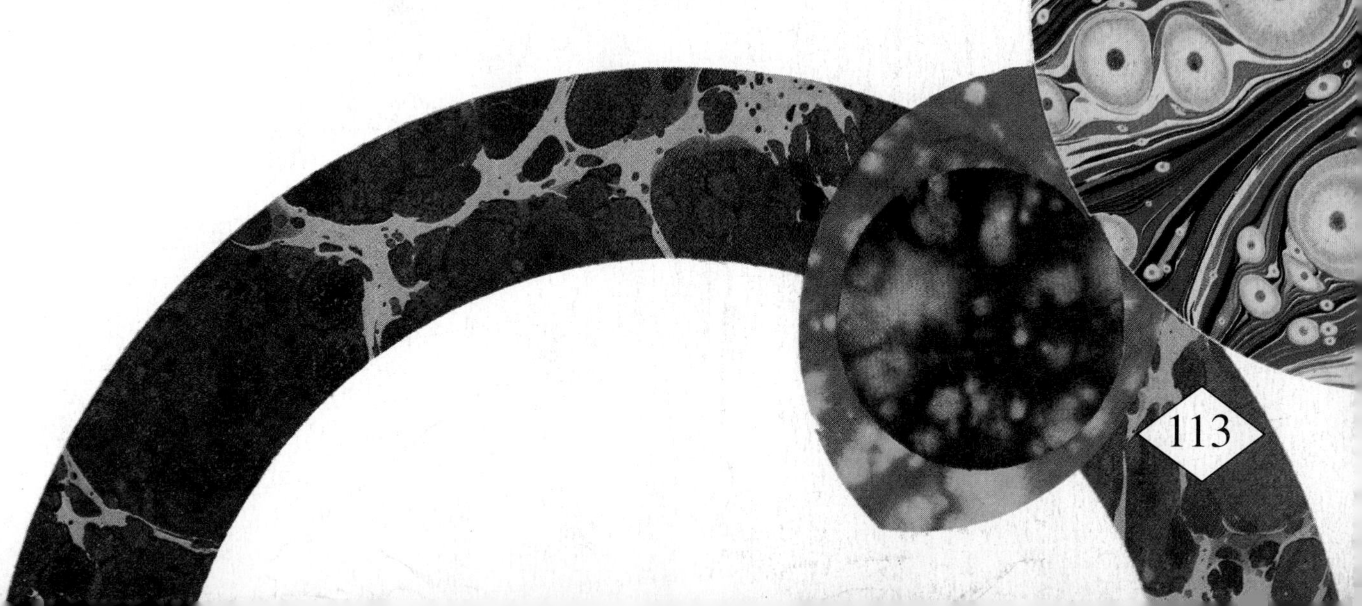

We look at stars
in Hungary—
back of the North Wind—
over the sea—
the Nutcracker laughs;
the Erl King calls;
a wish comes true;
the beanstalk falls;
the Western wind
blows sweet and low,
and Mother gives words
to worlds I know.

All of Our Noses Are Here

retold by Alvin Schwartz
illustrated by Karen Ann Weinhaus

The Browns went for a ride
in their rowboat. When the sun
began to go down, they rowed back
to shore.

"Everyone line up," said
Mr. Brown. "Let us see if anybody
fell out of the boat.

One is here.
Two are here.
Three are here.
And four are here."

"But we are five," said Mrs. Brown.

"I think I counted wrong," said
Mr. Brown. "I will count again.

One is here.
Two are here.
Three are here.
And four are here."

"Only four?" asked Mrs. Brown.

"Yes," said Mr. Brown. "One of
us is missing."

Mrs. Brown began to cry. So did the others.

"Why are all of you crying?" a fisherman asked.

"Five of us went rowing," said Mr. Brown. "But only four came back."

"Are you sure?" the fisherman asked.

Mr. Brown counted again.
Again he counted only four.

"I know what is wrong," said
the fisherman. "You forgot to count
yourself."

"I will try again," said
Mr. Brown.

"One is here.
Two are here.
Three are here.
And four are here.
And *five* are here.
And SIX are here!"

"But there should be five," said
Mrs. Brown.

"No," said Mr. Brown. "Now we are six."

"But I do not see anybody else," said Mrs. Brown.

They looked in the rowboat and
under the dock and up in the trees and
behind all the bushes, but they did not
find anyone.

"Come out! Come out! Whoever you
are!" Mr. Brown shouted.

The others joined in, but nobody came out.

When the fisherman heard the shouting, he went to see what was wrong.

"Now there are six of us, instead of five," said Mr. Brown. "But we cannot find this extra person."

"Are you sure there are six?" the
fisherman asked.

Mr. Brown counted again, and again
he counted six.

"You are doing it all wrong," said
the fisherman. "You counted yourself twice.
Let me show you the right way to count.

"Everybody, get down on your hands and knees. Now stick your noses into the mud and pull them out. Now count the holes your noses made."

125

Mr. Brown counted.

"One is here.
Two are here.
Three are here.
Four are here.
And *five* are here.

"All of our noses are here!" he
said. "Now we can go home."

Reader's Response ～ Did you
think this was a funny story? Tell why
or why not.

Library Link ～ *"All of Our Noses Are
Here"* came from a book called All of
Our Noses Are Here and Other Noodle
Tales. *Look for it in your library.*

Counting Rhymes

In this story, the fisherman helps the Browns learn to count. Could you teach someone to count? Maybe you could use this counting rhyme:

~

Here is the beehive. Where are the bees?
Hidden away where nobody sees.
Soon they come creeping out of the hive—
One! Two! Three! Four! Five!

~

Now that the Browns can count, they can play hopscotch or jump rope or maybe even baseball. Does counting help you play any games?

The Man, the Cat, and the Sky

by Barbara Juster Esbensen

Once upon a time there was a man.
He had a big white cat called Cream.
Their house and garden were by a river
in the country. In the morning they would
look at the green water. They would listen
to the blue wind blow over the grass. The
man would work in his garden. Cream
would watch the colored fish swim by
in the water.

One morning, the man was sad. This was the day the king and his friends would be playing games. The man wanted to go over the far hills to watch.

"I have never watched a king play games," he told Cream. "I'd like to go, but I don't have a horse or even a tiny cart. How could we get there? It's too far for us to walk."

Cream looked sad. He wanted to
see a king's cat. Maybe the king's
cat played games, too.

The man stopped and looked up
at the sky. It was as blue as could be.
Then the man saw a big puff of white.

"I see a big ship up there, Cream!"
he said. "Maybe that ship can take
us to see the king. What do
you think?"

Cream looked up. The ship was
blowing away.

"Oh, no!" said the man. "We'll
never get there! That ship can't
take us to see the king's games."

The man turned to look at the sky
again. "Now there are three white
horses in the sky," he said. "Would
you like to go with me to the king's
town, Cream? We could race like the
wind on the backs of these white horses.
One horse is for you, one horse is for
me. One horse will show us the way to
go. What do you think, Cream?"

Cream looked up. The horses
were blowing away.

"Oh, no!" said the man. "Now
we can't go to see the king on the
white horses!"

The man turned and looked up again.
There was nothing to see this time.
There was just the blue sky everywhere.
"We'll never see the king now,"
he told Cream.

Cream didn't hear the man's
sad words. He was listening to
something else. Cream could hear
singing far up the river. The man
listened, too.

It was the king! The king and
his friends were singing and blowing
their whistles. They came sailing
down the river. Their boats were
filled with bright red tents.

The man said, "It is the king!
Can this be true, Cream?"

Cream looked at the king and his black cat and the red tents. The wind did not blow them away.

The man sat down and took Cream on his lap. They watched the king and his friends play their games.

Reader's Response ~ Think about a cloud in the shape of something you could ride on. Where would you want it to take you?

Happy New Year!

Did you notice the emperor's beautiful green dragon boat? In China, the dragon is wise and stands for happiness and good luck.

Chinese New Year is a special holiday when Chinese people wish for happiness and good luck. They make a long dragon out of bamboo, paper, and silk. Fifty people get under the dragon and dance in the streets. They set off firecrackers. Families get together for huge dinners.

Here's how to say "Happy New Year" in Chinese: "Gung Hay Fat Choy!"

Stone Soup

retold by

Marjorie and Mitchell Sharmat

Three travelers were on their way home. They walked through woods. They walked through meadows.

"I need to eat," said the first traveler.

"I need to sleep," said the second traveler.

"I need to eat and sleep," said the third traveler.

They kept walking down the road until they came to a little town.

The people in the town saw the three travelers coming down the road.

"They will want a place to eat and sleep," said one man. "What can we do?"

"Tell them the wolf ate all our food! Then we can hide it," said a second man.

"We can hide it under our beds," said a third.

The people ran to hide their food. Some people hid it under their beds. Some people hid their food in other places.

The three travelers came to the town.

"We have walked and walked," they said to the people. "May we have some food and a place to sleep?"

"A wolf ate all our food," said the people in the town.

"All we have is water," they said.

"Water!" the three travelers said. "Good! We can make stone soup with that."

"What is stone soup?" asked
a woman.

"We'll show you," said the first
traveler. "Find us a big pot. Then
bring us some water and three, big
flat stones. Then get us some sticks
for a fire."

The people ran to get the pot, the water, and the sticks. Then they got the three, big, flat stones.

The travelers put the water and stones in the pot. Then they lit a fire under the pot. The fire cooked the stone soup.

The first traveler ate some soup. "M-m-m," he said. "The soup is good now. But green beans and a turnip would make it better."

"You're right! The wolf didn't eat all my green beans," said one woman. She ran home and took the beans from under her bed.

"And I have a turnip," said another woman. She ran home and took the turnip from under a basket.

The travelers put the beans and the turnip into the pot.

"M-m-m. Smell the soup! It's better now," said the second traveler. "But peas and beets would make it even better. Can you find some?"

"You're right! It does smell good," said a woman.

"The wolf didn't eat all my peas and beets," said one man. "I think I still have some at my house." And he ran to get them.

"Here," he said when he came back. He put the peas and beets into the pot.

"M-m-m. Smell the soup now. It's much better," said the third traveler. "But meat would make it much, much better. That's what the queen has in her soup."

"You ate with the queen?" the people asked in surprise.

Then they took all their food and put it into the pot.

"M-m-m!" said the people.

"M-m-m!" said the travelers. "This is soup fit for a queen!"

"You're wise men to make real soup from stones," said the people.

"Wise men need sleep," said the travelers.

"Take our beds!" said the people.

The three men went to sleep for the night. The next day they went off down the road to the next town.

Reader's Response ∿ What would you add to the stone soup to make it better?

What's in the Soup?

What is the strangest thing you can think of to put in soup? Have you ever had soup with peanuts in it? Or berries? How about a bird's nest?

Long ago Chinese cooks found that the nest of a bird called a swiftlet made delicious soup. You can taste Bird's Nest Soup in restaurants today.

Many cooks add a bit of this and a bit of that to their soups. One cook makes Refrigerator Soup. (No, he doesn't put a refrigerator in it!) He uses all the leftovers in his refrigerator to make soup.

What is your favorite soup? Do you know everything that's in it?

Alanike
and the
Storyteller

written by Donita Creola
illustrated by Jerry Pinkney

Alanike was a little girl who lived in a small village in Africa. She went to the village school every day. She worked hard. She wanted to know everything about everything. Sometimes Alanike worked so hard there was no time to play with the other boys and girls.

153

One day Alanike came home from school looking tired.

Alanike's grandfather hugged her.
"Cheer up, Alanike," he said. "Listen.
Do you hear the talking drums?
They are saying that the storyteller
will tell stories this very night.
We'll go and listen to him.
His stories will cheer you up."

BOOM
PUM
PUM
BOOM

After dinner Alanike and her grandfather took the long path to the storyteller's house. They could hear the drums calling the people in from their work and play.

The storyteller told his stories as
he had heard them when he was a boy.
His stories were about people who lived
in Alanike's village long ago.

There were stories about times when
there was not enough rain. There were
stories about times when there was a lot
of food and dancing.

The story Alanike liked best was
about a little boy named Bola. Bola
had lived in her village long ago. He had
worked so hard in school that he had no
friends. He didn't have time to play or to
have fun. Alanike thought that she knew
a little girl just like Bola. Alanike
listened to every word. She didn't want
the story to end.

The stories were over too soon.
She walked back to her house
hand in hand with her grandfather.

"Alanike," said her grandfather,
"you are smiling now. Tell me what
the storyteller said to bring back
your smile."

"Oh, Grandfather," said Alanike.
"The storyteller told me not to work
so hard that I forget to save time
for my friends."

From that day on Alanike still
worked hard. She still wanted to learn
everything about everything. But she
always saved time for her friends.

Reader's Response ∼ Think of a
story that made you smile. Tell the name of
the story and why it made you happy.

King of the Jungle:
A Story from Africa

In Africa, the leopard was king of the jungle. When it was time for a new king, the leopard said, "Whoever throws a spear and counts to ten before it hits the ground will be king."

The elephant tried. So did the lion and the gorilla. Each counted: "One, two, three, four . . ." and the spear fell.

When the antelope wanted to try, all the animals laughed. She threw the spear. Before it fell she quickly counted, "Five, Ten!"

All the animals shouted, "No fair!"

But the leopard said, "I never told you *how* to count to ten. Antelope will be a great ruler." And so she was.

Lee Bennett Hopkins
INTERVIEWS

Jerry Pinkney

This is Jerry Pinkney. He draws pictures of many things. He draws pictures for books. He draws pictures for stamps too.

These two stamps show pictures of famous Americans. One stamp shows Harriet Tubman. The other stamp shows Dr. Martin Luther King, Jr.

"My first love is drawing pictures for books," says Pinkney. "I hope that my pictures will help others want to read and look at books."

163

"As a child I drew everything," he said. "In school I drew and drew. My drawings made me feel special. I never thought I would grow up one day to be an artist. My mother always told me that I could be anything I wanted to be."

"I work with a pencil in one hand and an eraser in the other. I begin with a simple drawing," says Mr. Pinkney.

"If I don't like something that I draw, I erase it. Then I do it all over again. I work on it until I am happy with the drawing."

You saw some of Mr. Pinkney's drawings in "Alanike and the Storyteller." You can also look in the library for books with Mr. Pinkney's pictures:

The Patchwork Quilt
   by Valerie Flournoy
Wild Wild Sunflower Child Anna
   by Nancy White Carlstrom

Reader's Response ∾ Mr. Pinkney says, "If I don't like something that I draw, I erase it." What do you do if you don't like something that you draw?

Some Special Stamps

You have seen some stamps Jerry Pinkney made for the Post Office. Here are a few stamps some other artists made.

JACKIE ROBINSON—Jackie Robinson was the first African American to play on a modern-day major league baseball team.

PUEBLO ART—This stamp celebrates the art of the Pueblo people, a group of Native Americans.

CIRCUS—Many people have fun at the circus. Why not have a stamp for something that is so much fun?

PROJECT MERCURY—This stamp celebrates the first American to travel in space.

If you made a stamp, what picture would you put on it?

The Three Wishes

by Verna Aardema

Fritz and Anna lived on a farm.
It was a small farm. It was also very
dry, and things did not grow well.
So Fritz and his wife, Anna, were poor.

One day there was a tap, tap, tap on
the door. A woman had come to the farm.
She had been walking most of the day,
and she was hungry. She asked Fritz
and Anna to give her something to eat.
Fritz and Anna had a pot of soup.
They let the woman come in to eat.

"Thank you," said the
"You have been most kin
you three wishes. Remer
wishes wisely. Each wi
come true."

"Thank you," said Fritz.

"Thank you very much," said Ann

The woman left.

169

soon as the woman was outside
oor, Anna said, "Three wishes!
, Fritz, I've never been so happy!
We can have anything we want!"

Fritz said, "Let's have one wish
for you, and one wish for me. Then
we will have one wish left for the
two of us together."

"I like that," said Anna. "It
will be fun to have one wish that
is all mine."

For most of the day, Fritz and
Anna talked about the three wishes they
would make. They talked long after it was
time to eat again, and they forgot to
cook. They began to get hungry.

By the time Anna and Fritz made
soup, they were both very, very hungry.
As they sat down to eat, Fritz said, "I
wish we had a sausage to go with this
soup."

And there on the table was a
great big brown sausage!

"Oh, Fritz," said Anna, "there
goes your wish! And we have only
ONE sausage! I wish we had many,
many sausages."

There was Anna's only wish!

PUM, PUM, PUM! Great big sausages
rained down on them. They both ducked
and tried to get the sausages off them.

"Enough! Enough!" cried Anna.
"Get the sausages off me!"

"I can't help you," said Fritz. "I can't get the sausages off me!"

PUM, PUM, PUM, came the sausages. Soon the sausages were all around them.

"What can we do?" asked Anna, from under the sausages.

From under the sausages, Fritz said, "Let's eat them."

"Don't talk that way," said Anna.
"This is not funny! I've had enough
sausages. What can we do to get
out of this?"

"Well," said Fritz, "your wish
is gone, and mine is gone. But together
we have one wish left. Let's WISH to
get out from under the sausages."

Then they both said, "We wish
the sausages would go away."

Just as they had come, the
sausages went away. There were no
sausages anywhere! The big sausage
was also gone from the table.

Fritz and Anna were at the table,
with only the soup to eat.

"Oh, Fritz," said Anna, "I am
so sad! Here we are without any
more wishes."

"Anna," said Fritz, "we were happy
before the woman came. We can be
happy again. Most of all, I wish we had
a sausage to eat with this soup."

"Oh, Fritz," said Anna, "I don't
want to SEE a sausage for a long time!"

Reader's Response ∽ Pretend you
are Fritz or Anna. How do you feel when it
begins raining sausages? How do you feel
when you use your last wish and you are left
with nothing?

Library Link ∽ *If you liked this story
by Verna Aardema, look for her book*
Why Mosquitoes Buzz in People's Ears.

A Thinking Place

Like many children, Verna Aardema had a place where she liked to go and think. Do you have a special thinking place?

Verna liked to sit on an old log near a swamp. She sat there and thought. Sometimes she thought of ideas for stories.

When she grew up, she wrote stories for children. She began by telling stories to her small daughter. She had to! The child would eat only while listening to a story.

What story is your favorite story to tell?

TELL ME
A STORY, MAMA

by *Angela Johnson*
pictures by *David Soman*

Tell me a story, Mama, about when you were little.

What kind of story, baby?

Just any old story. How 'bout the time you lived in a little white house across the field from that mean old lady?

Meanest woman I've ever known, too, baby!

She was so mean that she used to holler out her window at you and Aunt Jessie when you passed her house every morning.

You weren't afraid of her, though.

No sir, I was not.

One day she scared Aunt Jessie so bad by letting her old bulldog out to bark at you all that Aunt Jessie cried all the way home.

You went back and threw mud on her white picket fence.

I sure had a temper . . .

Grandmama made you apologize,
but she kissed you hard on the head
and gave you an extra sweet roll
after dinner that night.

Your grandmama makes the best sweet rolls!

Is Grandmama going to stay here forever, Mama?
Just stay here and be Grandmama
forever to me?

She won't be here forever, baby,
but long enough for you never to forget
how much she loves you.

Did Grandmama squeeze you tight
when you were her little girl,
like she does me?

Uh-huh.

You were lucky, too, Mama.

Yes, I was.

Remember the time when you were little
and you found that puppy with no tail
by the side of the road?

Poor little thing . . .

You kept it hidden in your sweater, huh, Mama?

We had three dogs already.

You kept it hidden until it got hungry
and started to cry.
Grandmama didn't say anything.
She took that little puppy from you and
wrapped it up in her apron. She gave him milk
and then let him live in the milk crate
with your old baby blanket.

From one baby
to another,
she said.

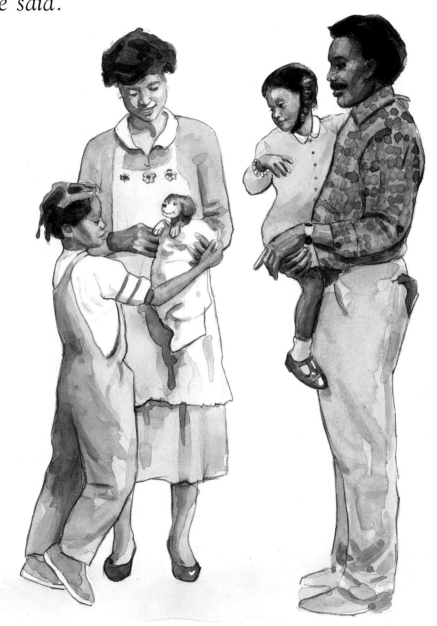

Do all animals have babies, Mama?

Yes they do, the females at least.

Puppies, huh?

No sir!

Aunt Jessie is the baby in your family.

Yes, she is.

Why did Grandmama and Grandaddy send
you and Aunt Jessie off to St. Louis when
you were both younger than me? Alone,
on a train?

*They had to work. And your great-aunt
Rosetta was lonely for children. Hers were all
grown up. Jessie and me, we kept her
company for a few months.*

Did your mama and daddy
miss you?

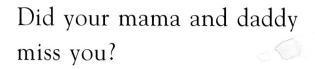

Like you'd miss the sun, baby.
We missed them, too,
but we loved Aunt Rosetta.

Aunt Jessie cried when the train pulled
out of the station and you couldn't see
Grandmama and Grandaddy anymore.

She cried all over me!

It's all right to cry, though.
Right, Mama?

If you feel like it, it's okay.

I feel like it sometimes, like when my best
friend Cory moved away. I did cry then.
I bet Cory cried, too.

I'll bet he did.

Would you cry if I moved away, Mama?

Yes, I will . . .

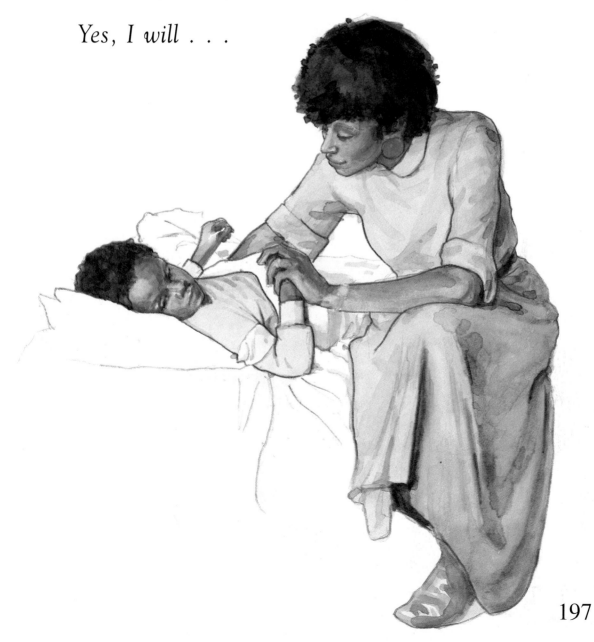

Grandmama cried when you moved away, Mama. She cried so hard that everybody at the airport looked at her and Grandaddy bought her flowers and a candy bar.

I remember.

I like it when you tell me stories, Mama.
Tell me more tomorrow.

Okay, baby. More stories tomorrow.

Reader's Response ❧ Why do you
think this little girl likes hearing the
stories her Mama tells?

Browsing for Books

A Place to Read

Do you ever " curl up with a good book "? It is something almost everyone does from time to time. When you are tired, a book can be your very best friend.

Many people have special places where they go to read their books, or just to look at the pictures in them. Do you? Beds are *wonderful* places to read when it's cold and you want to stay cozy and warm. The soft grass under a shady tree can be a fine place to stay cool with a good book. You can also keep a book in the car for the times when there's nothing to look at out the window. Sometimes it's nice to snuggle up to someone older who can read a book *to* you.

The most important thing is not where you read, but that you read something every day. Books can be your friends for life.

Dreams

EZRA JACK KEATS

201

It was hot.
After supper Roberto came
to his window to talk with Amy.
"Look what I made in school today—
a paper mouse!"

"Does it do anything?" Amy asked.

Roberto thought for a while.
"I don't know," he said. Then he put
the mouse on the window sill.

203

As it grew darker, the city got quieter.
"Bedtime, Roberto," called his mother.
"Bedtime for you, too,"
other mothers called.
"Good-night, Amy."
"Good-night, Roberto."
"G-o-o-o-o-d-night!" echoed the parrot.
Soon they were all in bed.

Someone began to dream.

Soon everybody was dreaming—
except one person.

209

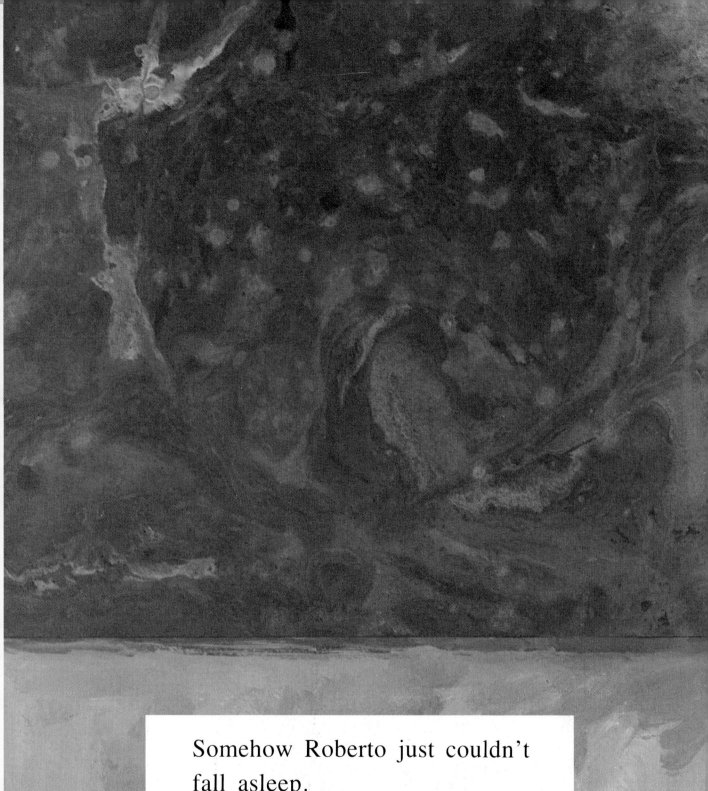

Somehow Roberto just couldn't
fall asleep.
It got later and later.

Finally he got up
and went to the window.
What he saw down in the street
made him gasp!

There was Archie's cat!
A big dog had chased him into a box.
The dog snarled.
"He's trapped!" thought Roberto.
"What should I do?"

Then it happened!
His pajama sleeve
brushed the paper mouse
off the window sill.
It sailed away from him.

218

Down it fell,
turning this way
and that,
casting a big shadow
on the wall.

The shadow grew bigger–
and bigger–

and BIGGER!
The dog howled and ran away.

The cat dashed across the street
and jumped through Archie's open window.
"Wow! Wait till I tell Archie
what happened!"
thought Roberto.
"That was some mouse!"
He yawned and went back to bed.

Morning came, and everybody
was getting up.
Except one person.

227

Roberto was fast asleep,
dreaming.

GLOSSARY

A

Americans

artist

ago Grandma was born a long time ago.

alone Mark sat alone in the room.

also Cats like fish. They also like milk.

Americans The people who live in the United States are Americans.

another Sue moved to another state.

anybody Anybody who likes to swim will like our pool.

anyone That dog will come to anyone.

anything When you are sick, you don't feel like doing anything.

anywhere Sara does not go anywhere without asking her mother.

artist The artist was painting.

230

B

baked Mother baked bread in the oven.

barn In winter, cows live inside a barn.

basket My dog likes to sleep in his own basket.

because It's wet because it just rained.

been Have you been to the lake?

before I brush my teeth before bed.

began Jake began to paint the wall.

better I liked this book better than that one.

birthday Lana baked a birthday cake for her mother.

blind Jeff cannot see because he was born blind.

boy Pete is the new boy in our class.

bubbles On a spring day, it is fun to blow bubbles.

baked

barn

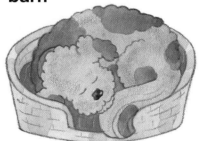

my dog's **basket**

Jake **began** to paint.

231

C

cart

We are **coming.**

Dad **cooked** dinner.

country

carry The suitcase was difficult to carry.

cart It's easy to move things in a cart.

child The small child held his mother's hand.

colored The fish were brightly colored.

coming Some friends are coming to play.

cooked Dad got the food ready and cooked dinner.

count Can you count from one to twenty?

country Rachel lives on a small farm in the country.

cousin Dan is my uncle. His son, Rob, is my cousin.

D

dancing Pat likes dancing to fast music.

dear The letter said, "Dear Pete, We miss you."

dinner Dinner is the last meal of our day.

drums Rick likes to beat on the drums.

ducklings The ducklings all stayed near the mother duck.

dancing

drums

ducklings

E

empty I need an empty box to pack all my books.

enough That was a big dinner. I had enough to eat.

erase If you make a mistake, erase it.

eraser This pencil has an eraser to rub out mistakes.

even We will have our family picnic even if it rains.

erase

233

everything Everything Debbie wears is pink.

everywhere John lost his ball. He looked everywhere for it.

extra Jane wanted the extra apple.

extra

F

famous Our shop is famous because so many people know about it.

far It takes a long time to walk to the park because it is far away.

Ann **felt** the fur.

felt Ann felt the cat's soft fur.

fingers Grandma's fingers are very thin.

fisherman That fisherman has caught lots of fish.

fisherman

forget Don't forget to feed the fish.

forgot Sara forgot to tie her shoes.

four There are two boys and two girls playing on the grass. Altogether there are four children.

four children

G

garden Corn, lettuce, and tomatoes grow in my garden.

girl The little girl was drawing.

goes Helen was running for the bus, but she missed it. "There goes the bus," she said.

goldfish Carol won a goldfish at the fair.

good-by As she left, Nancy kissed her grandpa good-by.

goodness When Grace saw a green man in her garden, she said, "Goodness, what a surprise!"

grandfather My grandfather, my mother's father, has lots of grandchildren.

great We have a great number of books in our house.

guitar We like to sing as our teacher plays the guitar.

garden

girl

There **goes** the bus.

guitar

235

horse

hugged

island

knees

H

horse My sister likes to ride her horse.

hugged Her mother held Meg close and hugged her.

hungry Rick was hungry at lunch time.

I

island We travel to the island by boat.

K

knees Judy scraped her knees when she fell on the sidewalk.

knew Tony knew the names of all his classmates.

236

L

learn Bob would like to learn how to play the drums.

letter Tim wrote his friend a letter.

library You can get good books from the library.

like We all like to go swimming in the summer.

listen Fred likes to listen to music.

lived Benita lived in the city.

lonely Amos felt lonely after he moved to a new town.

letter

library

M

most We have been painting this room for days, and most of it is done now.

move Greg's books were all over the table. I asked him to move them.

moved Grandma used to live near us, but she moved away.

moving

moving Tom was moving to the new house across the street.

must Dan must be on time for class.

N

Dad reads the **news.**

news Dad reads the newspaper to find out the news.

night The moon and the stars can be seen at night.

nose Jack bumped his nose on the slide.

nothing The cat licked the plate so clean that nothing was left on it.

night

O

only It was so hot that Bert was wearing only shorts.

own Jill was given her own lunch box.

P

pencil I like to draw with a pencil.

pitcher The pitcher was full.

places Our family visited many places on our vacation.

poor This poor cat has hurt its paw.

R

really José really likes to play outside.

remember Can you remember when you were two years old?

road The car drove along the road.

S

sausage I ate a sausage with my pancakes for breakfast.

second Beth came in first in the race, and Mark came in second.

share I share my pillow with my doll.

pencil

pitcher

road

sausage

239

sharks

stamps

stopped

summer

sharks We could see two sharks swimming out at sea.

should You should eat three meals a day.

sight Eric watched the plane until it flew out of sight.

simple Megan likes to make simple clothes.

slipped The bear slipped on the ice and almost fell down.

sorry Pete was sorry that he had broken the dish.

special Tim wore his special shirt to the birthday party.

splash The dog jumped into the lake with a splash.

stamps This letter needs more stamps.

stood When he saw the snake, Brad stood very still.

stopped The car stopped at the light.

straight This stick is crooked, but that one is straight.

summer It is warm in summer. We wear shorts every day.

T

table We set the table for dinner.

tadpoles We catch tadpoles to watch them turn into frogs.

talked Everyone talked and shouted at the same time.

tears John had tears in his eyes as he said good-by.

tents When it began to rain we ran into the tents to keep dry.

third Tad won the race. Matt was second, and Jed came in third.

through The dog walked through the hall and out the door.

together Let's have our picnic together.

town A town has many houses in it.

toy The dog likes to play with his toy.

travelers Many travelers enjoy camping.

turned Jerry watched as the top turned.

turnip You can buy a turnip in a vegetable store.

tadpoles

the dog's **toy**

The top **turned.**

turnip

village

whistles

twice Fred was at bat two times. He hit the ball twice.

U

---

used Meg used a broom to sweep the leaves off the porch.

V

---

village Helen lives in a village with only nine houses.

visit Tim went to visit his grandmother today.

W

---

whistles The man uses whistles to call his dogs.

whoever Whoever wins the race will win the prize.

wife Mr. Rodrigo lives with his wife, Mrs. Rodrigo.

wisely John is careful with his money and spends it wisely.

woman The little girl wants to grow up and become a woman.

woods Many trees grow in the woods.

words How many words are there in that big book?

write Joe likes to write many letters to his friends.

wrote Joe wrote four letters yesterday.

This book has **words.**

write

Y

---

yourself Do you ever talk to yourself?

ABOUT THE
Authors & *Illustrators*

Verna Aardema

Verna Aardema's first stories were
the ones she made up for her
daughter. Now her stories are read
by children all over the world.

Aliki

Aliki's full name is Aliki Liacouras Brandenberg. Aliki says, "I write two kinds of books—fiction (which comes from my own ideas) and nonfiction (which I must find out about from others)." She also draws pictures for books.

Barbara Juster Esbensen

Barbara Juster Esbensen is both an art teacher and an author. She likes to write poetry and stories for children. She also likes to help teachers help their students write poetry. She wants students to explore their own creative minds and use their ideas to write. She likes to think that a classroom is alive with language activity!

245

Langston Hughes

Langston Hughes wrote many
poems, plays, and songs for adults.
He also wrote poetry for children.
He started writing poetry in high
school. He liked to read books all
the time when he was little. He also
liked to listen to the stories that his
grandmother told him. He would sit
on her lap in a rocking chair and
listen to her stories for hours. As an
adult he traveled all over the world
to meet people, listen to their
stories, and then write about them.

Nikki Giovanni

Nikki Giovanni writes poetry. She says it is exciting to write for children and to read to children. She hopes her poetry reaches the hearts and minds of all children and even the adult who still has a bit of a child within.

Angela Johnson

Angela Johnson remembers that when she and her brother were children her father and grandfather would tell them a story almost nightly. She thinks she may have inherited her storytelling ability from them. "Some stories they'd tell us so often we could recite them by heart." She says that if they left out a word, her father or grandfather would fill it in for them. Her own Aunt Rosetta is the mama in *Tell Me a Story, Mama.* She thinks that many children enjoy recalling stories they have heard as children. *Tell Me a Story, Mama* was her first book, and it was named a Best Book of the Year by *School Library Journal.*

Ezra Jack Keats

Ezra Jack Keats wrote many books. He illustrated most of the books that he wrote. He began painting when he was about four years old. When he was little, he drew all over the top of the kitchen table. He said, "I filled up the entire table with pictures of little cottages, curly smoke coming out of the chimneys, men's profiles, and kids." He thought that he was going to get into trouble. But when his mom entered the room she said, "Did you do that? Isn't it wonderful!" Then she showed off his work of art to her neighbors. Children like the way he combined painting and collage in vivid colors for the illustrations in his books. He won many awards for his work.

Myra Cohn Livingston

Myra Cohn Livingston wrote her first book of poems when she was still in school. In her poems, she writes about the things people feel, see, and hear every day. Her poetry has won many awards.

Arnold Lobel

Arnold Lobel wrote and illustrated books for children. His books have won many awards. One thing he especially liked about being a writer was being able to make a character do just what *he* wanted to do.

James Marshall

James Marshall wrote and illustrated books for children. He also illustrated books for other authors. He won many awards for his books. Children love his George and Martha stories about two hippopotamuses.

Else Holmelund Minarik

Else Holmelund Minarik began writing when she was a teacher. When she taught first grade, she could not find enough books for her students. She then began to write them herself. Children loved the books she wrote about Little Bear and his family. Now she writes books about other animals, too.

Jerry Pinkney

Jerry Pinkney has illustrated many children's books, designed record covers, drawn pictures for magazines, and designed eleven different stamps for the U.S. Postal Service. When he was in first and second grade, he often drew pictures in front of the class. Now he likes to use pencil sketches and watercolors when illustrating children's books. He has won many awards for his art work. When he draws pictures of people, he models his drawings after the children of his friends, his granddaughter, his granddaughter's friends, and even his wife and himself.

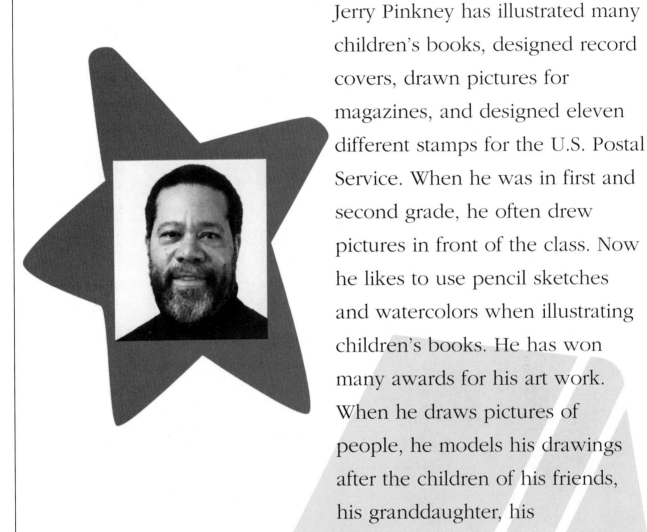

Anne Rockwell

Anne Rockwell writes books for children. She also illustrates books. She says she has a special place to write her books. It is a "secret writing room for me, with a window that looks up only into the trees. I have been having a wonderful time working in it."

Maurice Sendak

Maurice Sendak has written and illustrated many books. When he was a child, he drew many pictures indoors because his father was afraid he would get sick if he went outside. He has fond memories of the beautiful imaginative tales his father told him and his sister when they were young. He thinks the best children's books let a child use his or her imagination. Children can certainly use their imagination when reading Maurice Sendak's books!

Alvin Schwartz

Alvin Schwartz wrote many books for children. One of his favorite places to write was in a tool shed in his backyard. He liked to write funny stories. Often he would get ideas for his books from people who shared their stories with him.

Mitchell Sharmat

Mitchell Sharmat is both an author and an illustrator. He and his wife, Marjorie Sharmat, often work together writing children's books. They take turns suggesting ideas and words. His wife writes down the words and then reads them back. He thinks that children like his books because they are funny and make them laugh.

AUTHOR INDEX